WOLFGANG AMADEUS MOZART

CONCERTO

for Horn and Orchestra
D major/D-Dur/Ré majeur
K 412
with Facsimile of Fragment
K 494a

Ernst Eulenburg Ltd

London · Mainz · Madrid · New York · Paris · Tokyo · Toronto · Zürich

Mozart, Horn Concerto in D, K.V. 412

The D-major concerto for Horn, K.V.412 (386b in Einstein's new revision of the Köchel catalogue) consists of two movements, an Allegro and a Rondo-Allegro. The autograph of the completely orchestrated first movement in the " Öffentliche Wissenschaftliche Bibliothek " (formerly Preussische Staatsbibliothek) in Berlin also contains a sketch of the Rondo, which leaves little doubt that the two movements belong together. The Rondo however was finished only five years later ; hence Köchel mentions it once more as 514, and St. Foix discusses the two movements separately. Both movements originated in 1782 ; Einstein's new revision places them shortly after " Entführung " and immediately before the first of the string quartets dedicated to Haydn (G major), whereas according to Köchel, they were written considerably later than this string quartet, but still in 1782. It is remarkable that the orchestral accompaniment of the Rondo (completed in 1787) does not contain any bassoons, as the orchestra in the first movement consists of 2 Violins, Viola, Bass, 2 Oboes, and 2 Bassoons.

K.V.412 is strictly divided by its key signature from the other three Horn Concertos (K.V.417, 447, 495), which are all in E flat. But like the others it was also written for the former horn player of the Salzburg Orchestra, Ignaz Leutgeb (Leitgeb), whom Mozart's father met again in Vienna in 1777 as the owner of a cheese shop. Leutgeb, a sound horn player, still appeared occasionally as a soloist in the concert hall in Vienna, and for this reason had asked Mozart in 1777 for a " Concert." Mozart seems to have taken a special delight in teasing Leutgeb, for many stories have been handed down to us

Mozart, Hornkonzert D-dur KV. 412

Das D-dur-Konzert für Horn, das die in Einsteins Neubearbeitung des Köchelverzeichnisses nach 386b versetzte Köchel-Nummer 412 trägt, besteht aus zwei Sätzen, einem Allegro und einem Rondo-Allegro, die schon deshalb zusammenzugehören scheinen, weil dem in der " Oeffentlichen Wissenschaftlichen Bibliothek " (früher Preussische Staatsbibliothek) in Berlin liegenden Autograph des vollständig instrumentierten ersten Satzes eine Skizze des Rondos beigegeben ist, das allerdings erst fünf Jahre später fertig ausgearbeitet worden ist (und bei Köchel unter 514 nochmals gesondert angeführt wird; St. Foix bespricht die beiden Sätze deshalb getrennt). Das Entstehungsjahr beider Sätze ist 1782 ; nach Einsteins revidierter Einordnung stehen sie nunmehr kurz nach der " Entführung " und unmittelbar vor dem ersten der Haydn gewidmeten Streichquartette (G-dur), während sie bei Köchel beträchtlich hinter das letztere—doch immer noch ins Jahr 1782—zu stehen kommen. Auffallend ist, dass das (1787 vollendete) Rondo in der Begleitung auf die Fagotte des ersten Satzes verzichtet ; die Instrumentation des ersten Satzes lautet : 2 Violinen, Viola, Bass, 2 Oboen, 2 Fagotte.

Unser Werk ist durch die Tonart von den andern drei Hornkonzerten Mozarts (KV.417, 447, 495), die alle in Es-dur stehen, scharf geschieden, aber auch es ist für den ehemaligen Hornisten der Salzburger Kapelle Ignaz Leutgeb (Leitgeb), den Mozarts Vater 1777 in Wien als Inhaber einer Käserei wieder traf, geschrieben. Leutgeb, ein tüchtiger Hornist, trat in Wien noch gelgentlich als Solist in Konzerten auf und hatte sich dazu 1777 von Mozart " ein Concert " erbeten. Mozart

about the jokes which he had at his expense (for details about this and about Leutgeb generally see the foreword to K.V.447 and also the forewords to K.V.417 and 495 in the Edition Eulenburg). In the original MS of the Rondo Mozart leaves free rein to his exuberance (cf. Abert II, p. 50): Already the tempo in the horn part is marked Adagio, whereas the orchestra bears the correct tempo indication Allegro. Then follows a whole sequence exhortations, indications, comic and ironic exclamations, which finally resolve in the sigh : " finisci ? grazie al ciel ! basta, basta !" The whole is a true example of Mozart's sense of humour, as can be seen from Abert's detailed description. The Rondo, like the Finales of the other horn concertos, is of the " hunt " type, full of freshness and charm.

For more details about the literature on Mozart's Horn Concertos see our bibliography to K.V.447. Also : St. Foix III, pg. 328f (No. 495) and IV, pg. 240 (No. 514) ; Complete Edition, Editor's Note to XII No. 16. According to Köchel-Einstein the autograph of the complete Rondo was in the possession of Frau Baroni di Cavalcabò in Graz, who inherited it from Mozart's son. It bears the date " Vienna, Venerdì Santo li 6 Aprile 1797." Köchel-Einstein is of the opinion that the date has been postponed by ten years " just for fun." Or was it just a mistake on Mozart's part ? 6th April 1787 was really Good Friday, but 6th April 1797 was a Thursday.

Köchel's Appendix (No. 98a) contains the E major fragment (91 bars) of a horn concerto, the orchestral accompaniment of which consists of strings, 2 oboes and 2 horns. This MS is also in the Offentliche Wissenschaftliche Bibliothek in Berlin, from whom we have permission to append a facsimile to this edition. Einstein considers this fragment to be

scheint an Leutgeb mit Vorliebe sein Mütchen gekühlt zu haben, denn es ist allerhand Schabernak, den er mit ihm getrieben hat, überliefert (Näheres über dies sowie über Leutgeb siehe in der Einleitung zu KV.447 und vgl. dazu auch die Einleitungen zu 417 und 495 in der Edition Eulenburg). Im Originalmanuskript unseres Rondos lässt Mozart seinem Uebermut die Zügel schiessen (vgl. Abert II, S.50) : Gleich das Tempo ist in der Hornstimme mit Adagio bezeichnet, während beim Orchester richtig Allegro steht, und dann folgt eine ganze Szene mit Zurufen, Vorschriften, komischen und ironischen Ausrufen, die am Schluss in dem erlösten Seufzer gipfelt : " finisci ? grazie al ciel ! basta, basta !" Man muss das Ganze bei Abert nachlesen ; es ist ein echtes Stückchen des Mozart'schen Humors. Der Charakter des Rondos ist wie bei den Finales der andern Hornkonzerte jagdartig ; wie der erste Satz ist es ein frisches, reizvolles Musizierstück.

Für die Literatur im Einzelnen sei auf unsere Literaturangaben zu KV. 447 verwiesen. Dazu : St. Foix III. S.328f (No. 495) und IV. S.240 (No. 514). Gesamtausgabe Revisionsbericht zu XII No. 16. Das Autograph des vervollständigten Rondos befand sich laut Köchel-Einstein früher bei Frau Baroni di Cavalcabò in Graz aus dem Nachlass von Mozarts Sohn ; es trägt das Datum " Vienna, Venerdi santo li 6 Aprile 1797" wohl " spasseshalber " um zehn Jahre hinausgeschoben, meint Köchel-Einstein*).

In Köchels Anhang ist unter No. 98a das E-dur-Bruchstück eines Konzertes für Horn (91 Takte) enthalten, das in der Begleitung neben den Streichern 2 Oboen und 2 Hörner aufweist. Auch es ist heute in der Oeffentlichen Wissenschaftlichen Bibliothek zu Berlin, mit deren Genehmigung wir es dieser Ausgabe im Anhang als Facsimile

iv

the Andante(2nd movement) of K.V.412 and says : " It is hardly conceivable that Mozart did not compose a second movement to this concerto. I am convinced that Anh. 98a is the beginning of this missing middle movement. Hence I put this fragment in its place, although, like the completed Rondo, it may not have been written till April 1787."

WILHELM MERIAN

beigeben. Einstein sieht darin den Andante-Mittelsatz unseres Konzertes und sagt : " Es ist schwer glaublich, dass Mozart zu diesem Konzert keinen Mittelsatz komponiert haben sollte. Ich bin überzeugt, dass Anh. 98a der Beginn dieses fehlenden Mittelsatzes ist, und setze daher das Fragment an diese Stelle, obgleich es, wie das beendigte Rondo, auch erst im April 1787 geschrieben sein könnte."

WILHELM MERIAN

*Oder war es ein Versehen Mozarts. Der 6. April 1787 war tatsächlich Karfreitag (der 6. April 1797 ein Donnerstag).

CONCERTO

I

W. A. Mozart
1756-1791

Köchel N.º 412 u. Anh. 98a

4

6

8

16

18

E. E. 6027

20

II

22

TUTTI

28

80
TUTTI

SOLO

34

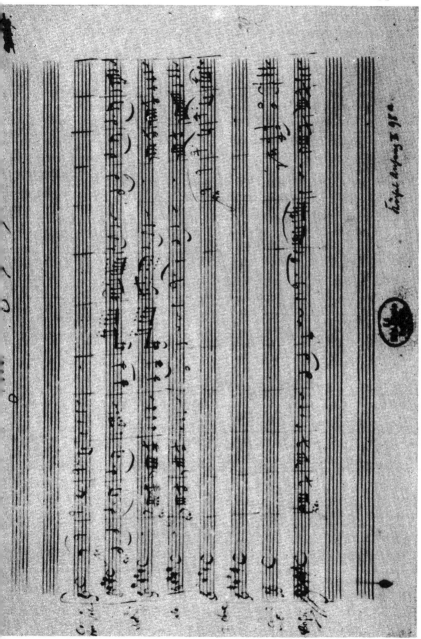

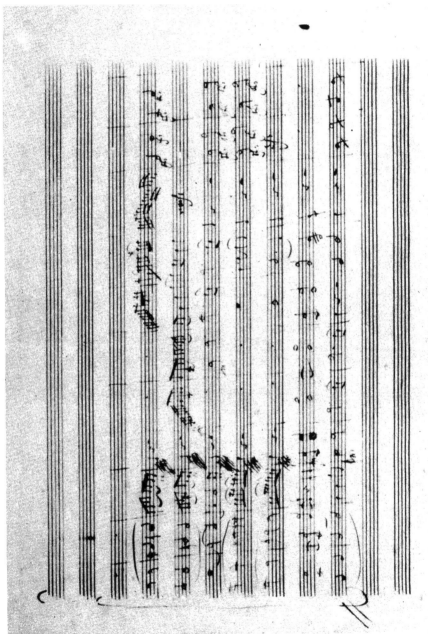

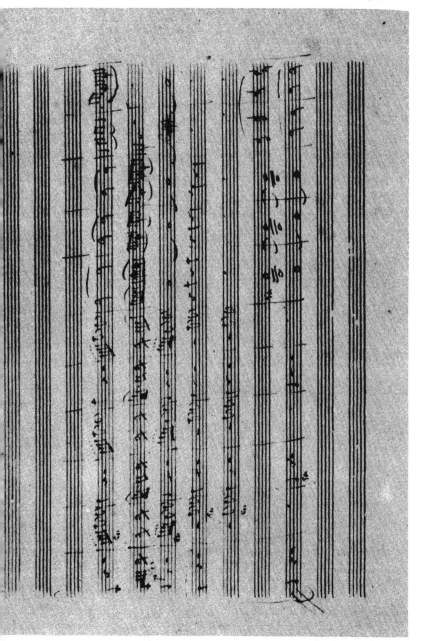

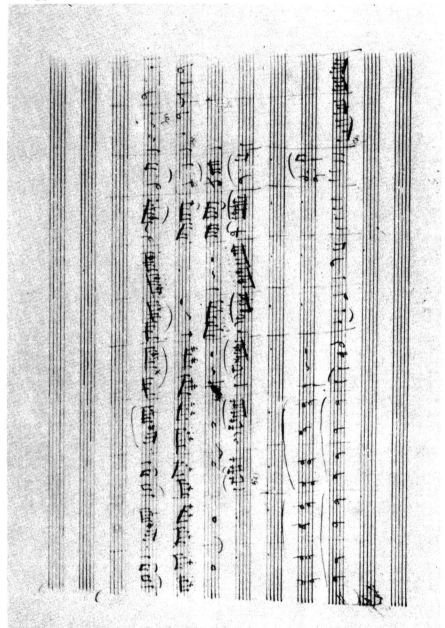

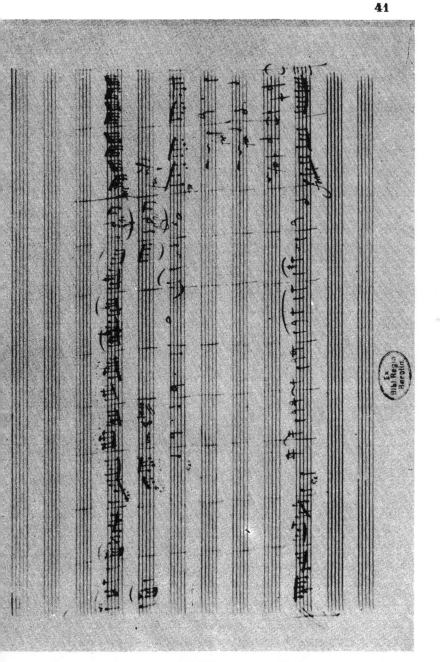

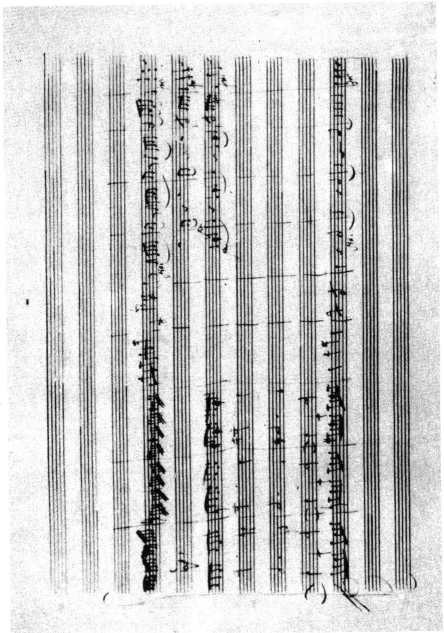

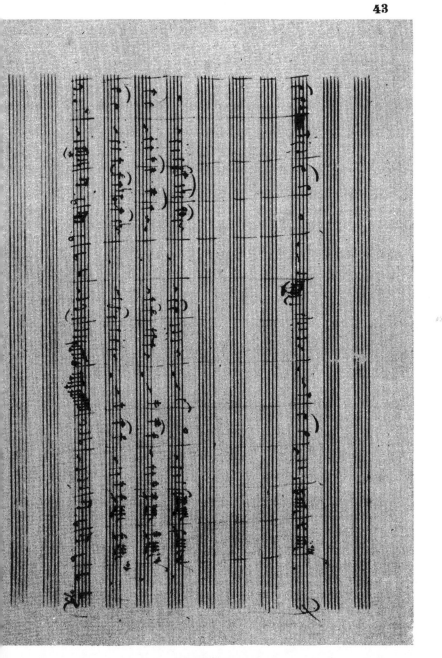

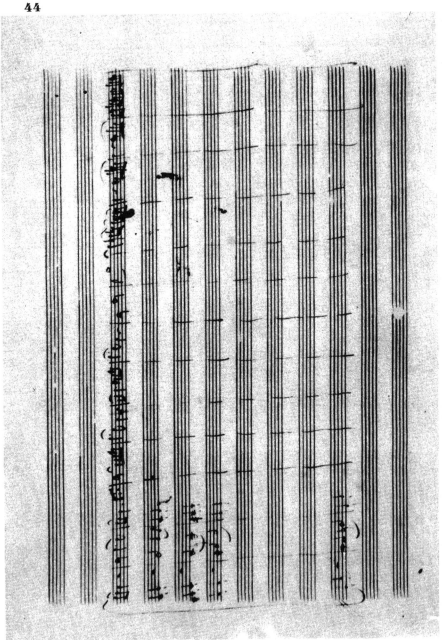

44